AGES 6-7
Key Stage 1

Gold Stars®

English

tree   house

PaRRagon

Bath · New York · Cologne · Melbourne · Delhi
Hong Kong · Shenzhen · Singapore · Amsterdam

Helping your child

⭐ The activities in this book will help your child learn about English. Pictures provide hints and clues to support their reading.

⭐ Your child will gain the confidence to: read and write independently, read and check for sense and spelling, use comprehension skills effectively, use capital letters and full stops, use dictionary skills and alphabetical order.

⭐ Your child will learn about: colour and number words, months of the year, speech marks and apostrophes, nouns, verbs and adjectives.

⭐ Set aside time to do the activities together. Do a little at a time so that your child enjoys learning.

⭐ Give lots of encouragement and praise. Use the gold stars as rewards and incentives.

⭐ The answers are on page 32.

Written by Betty Root and Monica Hughes
Educational Consultant: Stephanie Cooper
Illustrated by Adam Linley
Cover illustrated by Simon Abbot

This edition published by Parragon Books Ltd in 2014

Parragon Books Ltd
Chartist House
15–17 Trim Street
Bath BA1 1HA, UK
www.parragon.com

ISBN 978-1-4723-5675-8

Printed in China

Contents

Number words	4	Reading for meaning	19
Word endings	5	Speech marks	20
All about nouns	6	Missing letters	21
Adjectives	7	Writing postcards	22
Out and about	8	Speech bubbles	23
Dictionary	10	Reading instructions	24
Dictionary skills	11	Silly or sensible?	25
Using verbs	12	Odd one out	26
Quick quiz	13	Quick quiz	27
Months of the year	14	Opposites	28
Fill in the gaps	15	Finish the sentences	29
Descriptions	16	Word search	30
Compound words	17	Puzzle page	31
Making new words	18	Answers	32

Number words

Colour the balloons.

1 = red   **2** = purple   **3** = yellow   **4** = blue
5 = green   **6** = red   **7** = purple   **8** = yellow
9 = blue   **10** = green

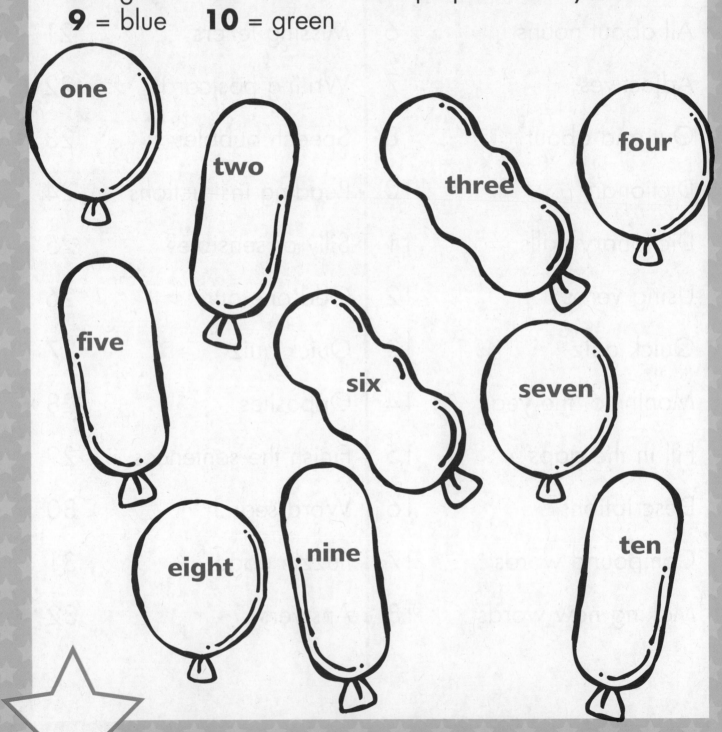

Note for parent: Your child is learning colour and number words in this activity.

Word endings

Look at the first picture in each row.
Draw a circle around two pictures in each row that have the same ending as the first.

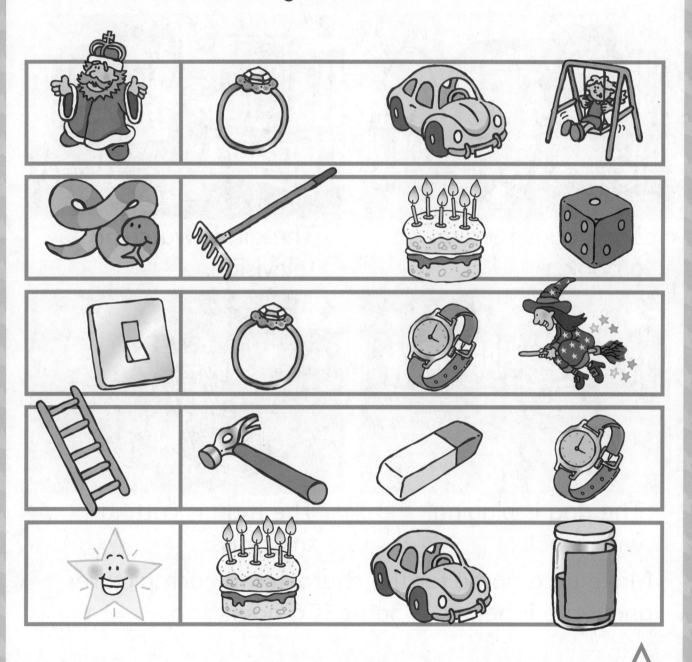

Note for parent: This activity encourages your child to listen carefully to word endings.

5

All about nouns

Words that name people, animals, things and places are called nouns. Read these sentences and draw a line under each noun.

1

The boy is reading a book.

2

The girl is watching television.

3

The dog is playing with a ball.

4

The man is cutting the grass.

Make up a name for the character in each picture and write it below. A name is a noun, too.

_____   _____

_____   _____

Adjectives

An adjective tells you more about someone or something.
Choose an adjective to fill in the missing words in the sentences below.

cold	windy	blue
happy	small	fresh

1. A ladybird is very _____ .

2. The leaves fell off the tree because it was _____ .

3. The sun was shining and the sky was _____ .

4. Dad had just picked the flowers so they were _____ .

5. The dog was _____ because he had a new ball.

6. It was _____ in the garden and there was ice on the pond.

Note for parent: Describing words are important as they are useful for your child to use in stories.

7

Look at the picture. Words are missing from some of the signs and labels. Use the words in the box opposite to fill in the spaces.

Note for parent: This activity reinforces the use of nouns, capital letters and labels for your child.

Café　　**Shoe shop**　　**Open**　　**Litter**
Main Street　　**Fish shop**　　**Sale**
Bus stop　　**Post box**　　**Telephone**

Dictionary

Try to write a label to go with each picture, then check your spelling in a dictionary.

Note for parent: Your child should be able to spell most or all of these words. The skill is using the dictionary.

Dictionary skills

A dictionary also tells you what words mean.
This is called a **definition**. Draw a line to join each
word to the correct definition.

	boy	A creature you read about in fairy tales.
	hutch	A black-and-white bird that cannot fly.
	monster	A tool that has sharp metal teeth.
	saw	A male child.
	penguin	A pet rabbit's home.

Now draw a picture for each word.

Note for parent: Your child is learning to problem-solve as they read and choose the right sentence that makes sense with each word.

11

Using verbs

What is each animal doing? Tick your answer.

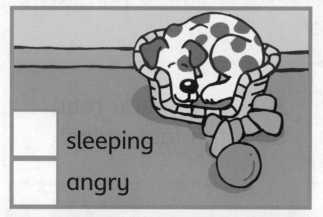

- [ ] sleeping
- [ ] angry

- [ ] happy
- [ ] licking

- [ ] running
- [ ] cold

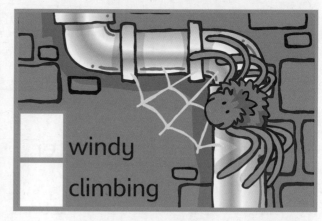

- [ ] windy
- [ ] climbing

- [ ] dirty
- [ ] swimming

- [ ] flying
- [ ] fresh

What are you doing now? _____

12

Read the words.
Write the number.

two	
six	
three	
eight	
ten	
four	
seven	
nine	
one	
five	

Join each word ending to a picture.

 ce

 ake

 ing

 er

 ar

 tch

Note for parent: This is a revision of some of the learning covered so far.

13

Months of the year

Class 2 have made a chart to show when the children have their birthdays.

January	February	March	April
Harry	Brian	Alison	Mohammed
Duncan	Jamilla		
May	**June**	**July**	**August**
Ellen	Mark	Oliver	Chloe
Paul	Lisa	Kerry	Polly
Zara	Ahmed		William
Ben			
September	**October**	**November**	**December**
	Sophie	Amy	Brendan
	Wendy		Daniel
			Sally
			Gail

1. When is Amy's birthday? _____
2. When is Harry's birthday? _____
3. When is Sophie's birthday? _____
4. When is Oliver's birthday? _____
5. Which month has no birthday? _____
6. Which months have the most birthdays?

_____

When is your birthday? _____

Note for parent: This activity helps your child to learn the months of the year.

Fill in the gaps

Use these letter sounds to fill in the gaps:
ai (nail) or **ea** (meat). Read the words
when you have made them.

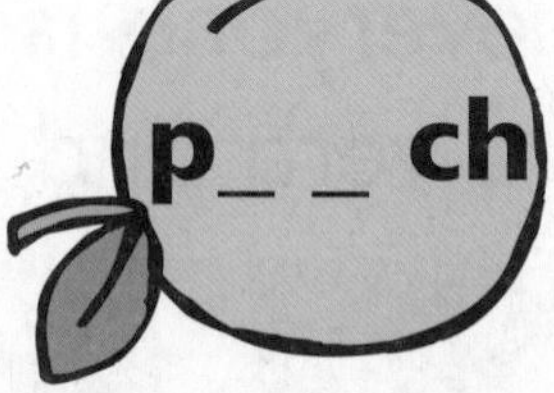

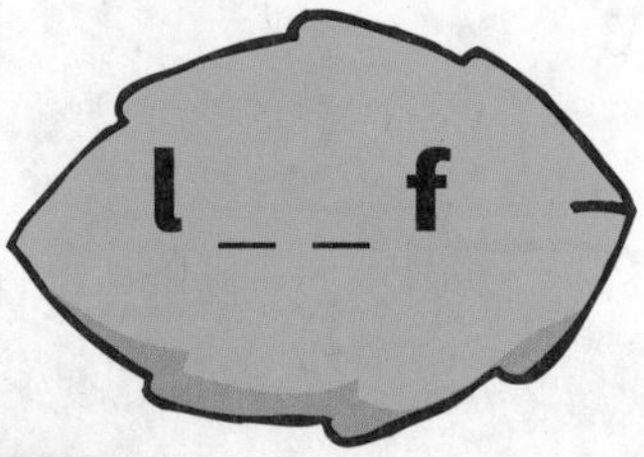

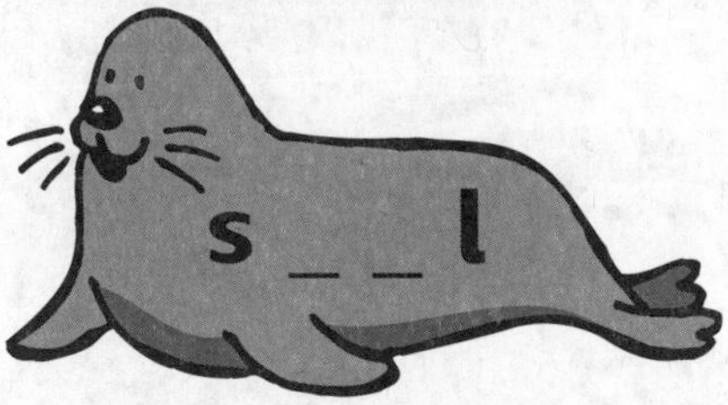

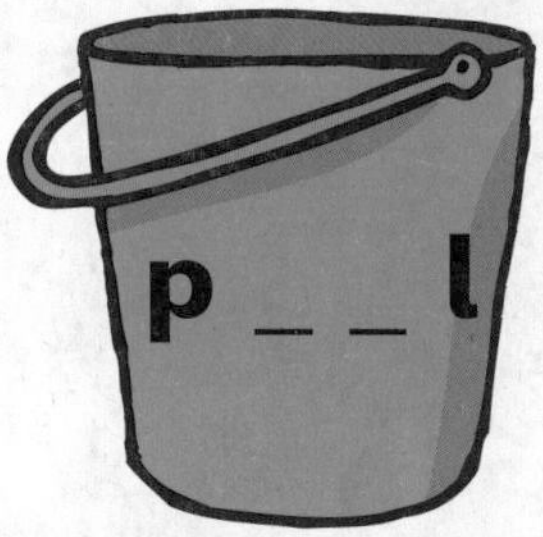

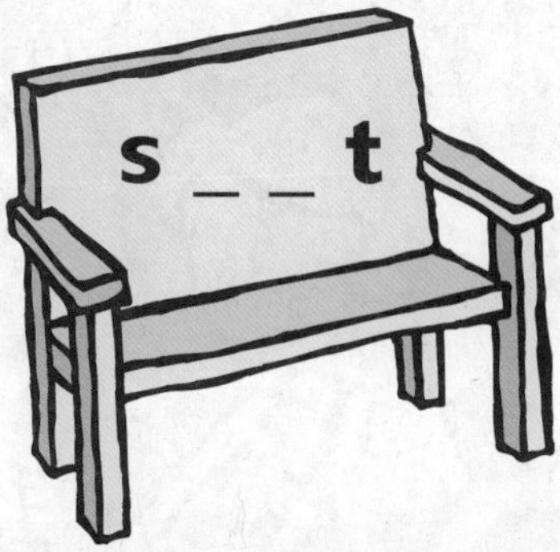

p_ _ ch

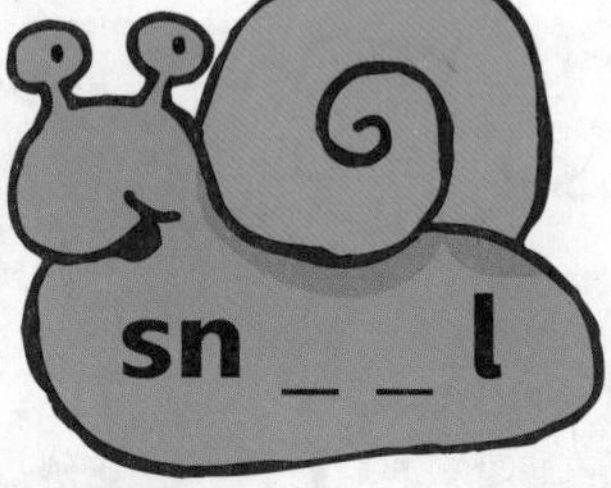

l_ _ f

sn _ _ l

s _ _ t

s _ _ l

p _ _ l

Now use these letters to fill the gaps:
oa (goat) or **ou** (house).

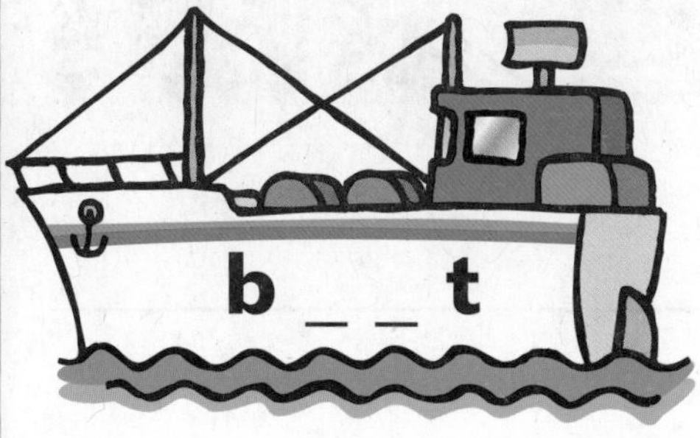

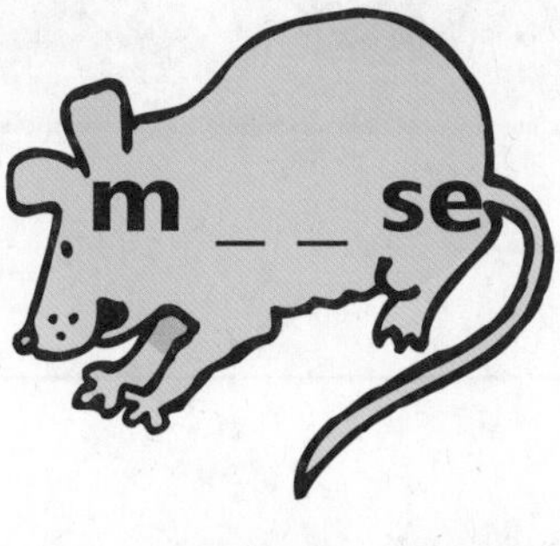

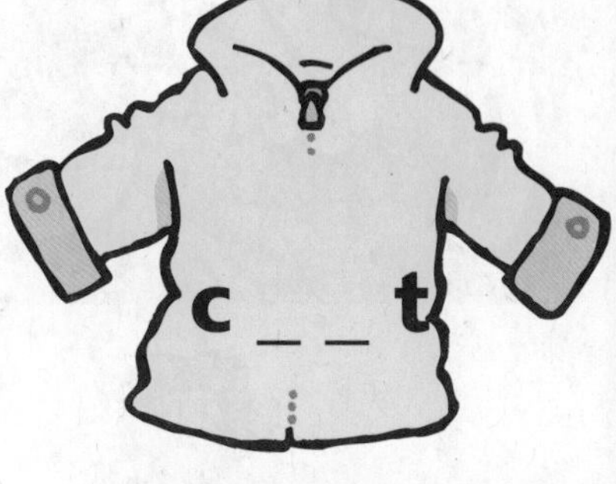

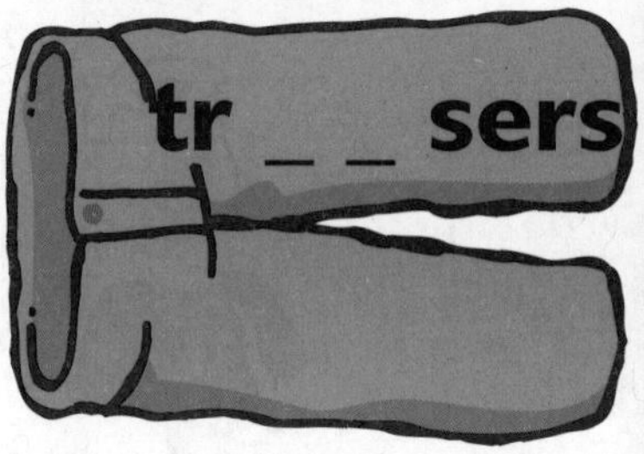

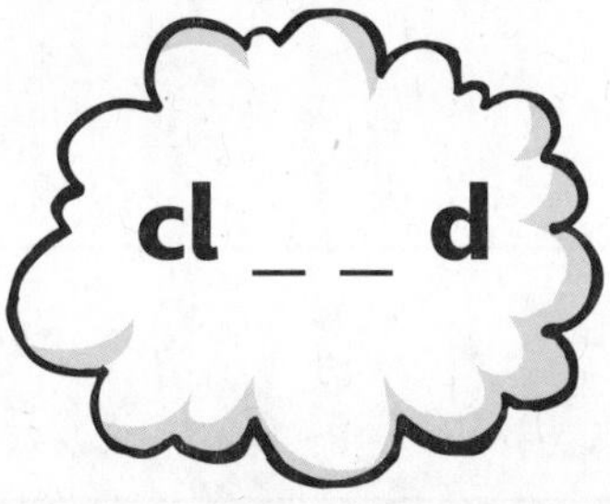

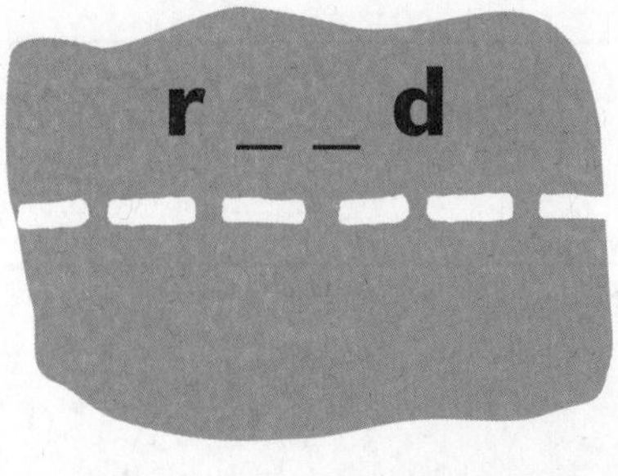

c_ _ t

b _ _ t

m _ _ se

tr _ _ sers

cl _ _ d

r _ _ d

Descriptions

Look at the picture. Write a sentence saying what everyone is doing. Try to include a noun, a verb and an adjective in your sentences.

_____

_____

_____

_____

_____

Note for parent: This activity helps your child learn how to describe people using proper sentences.

Compound words

You make a compound word by joining two smaller words together.

 **+** **=**

horse   **shoe**   **horseshoe**

Now try to make compound words from the words below:

1   star + fish = _____

2   water + fall = _____

3   home + work = _____

4   play + time = _____

5   tooth + brush = _____

6   foot + ball = _____

7   ear + ring = _____

8   book + mark = _____

Making new words

You can make new words by changing some of the letters in a word.

Change the **p** in **park** to **m** → **mark**
Change the **p** in **park** to **sh** → **shark**

Now make other new words, just by changing the first sound.

1. Change the **b** in **bear** to **p** → _____

   to **w** → _____

2. Change the **f** in **fire** to **w** → _____

   to **h** → _____

3. Change the **j** in **jaw** to **cl** → _____

   to **str** → _____

4. Change the **br** in **brown** to **cl** → _____

   to **cr** → _____

5. Change the **fl** in **flight** to **br** → _____

   to **kn** → _____

Note for parent: This activity helps your child to understand the composition of words.

Reading for meaning

Three children have made a list of what they have in their lunch box. Read the lists and then answer the questions.

Kelly
chicken sandwich
packet of crisps
apple
chocolate cake
can of fizzy drink

Sam
bottle of water
piece of cheese
yoghurt
banana
salad roll

Anna
yoghurt
carton of fruit juice
packet of raisins
cheese sandwich
chocolate biscuit

 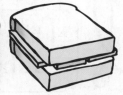  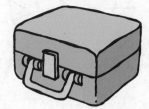

1. Who has a piece of fruit?_____
2. Who has a yoghurt?_____
3. Who has a sandwich?_____
4. Who has something made of chocolate?

_____
5. Who likes cheese?_____
6. Who has a packet of something?

_____
Make a separate list of what you would like to have in your lunch box.

Note for parent: This activity helps your child to make sense of lists and to use information to answer questions.

Speech marks

Read what each animal says.

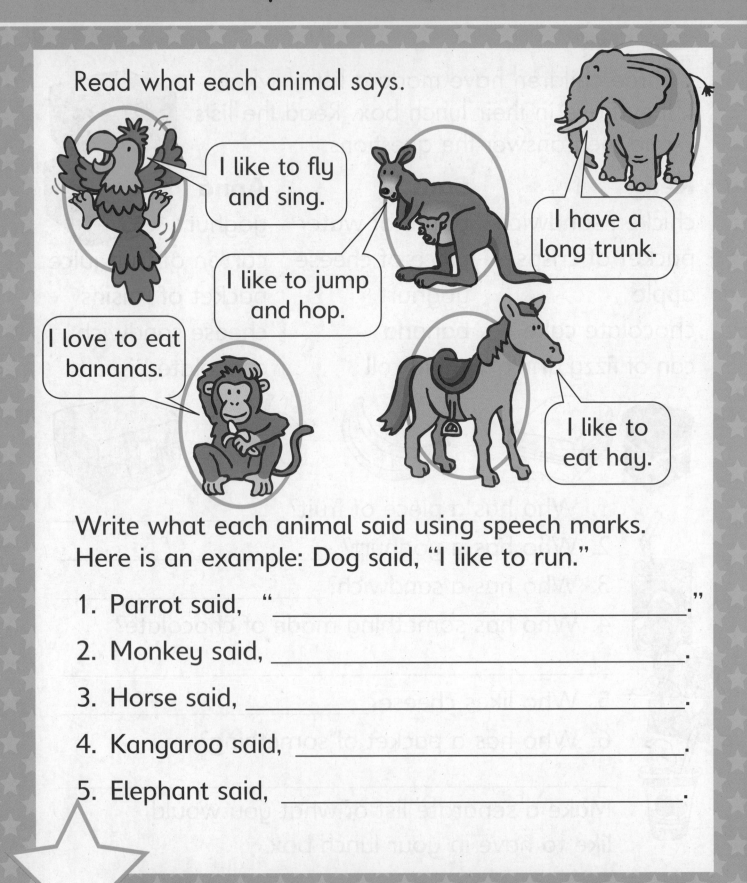

I like to fly and sing.

I like to jump and hop.

I have a long trunk.

I love to eat bananas.

I like to eat hay.

Write what each animal said using speech marks.
Here is an example: Dog said, "I like to run."

1. Parrot said, "_____."

2. Monkey said, _____.

3. Horse said, _____.

4. Kangaroo said, _____.

5. Elephant said, _____.

Sometimes when we talk to people
we do not say every word.

I am = I'm   It is = It's

Join the words on the left side of
the page to the smaller words on the right.

is not	I'd
cannot	won't
I would	isn't
I am	I'm
will not	you've
you have	can't

Write these sentences again using smaller words
instead of the underlined words:

<u>I would</u> like to see you but <u>I am</u> ill. I <u>cannot</u> go out
but <u>I would</u> like to see you if <u>you have</u> time and it
<u>is not</u> too far for you to come.

_____

_____

_____

_____

Note for parent: Try to explain how an apostrophe is always used in these shortened versions.

21

Write a postcard to a relative (for example your granny, a cousin, an uncle) telling them about your school. Plan what you want to say before you start writing.

Dear _____

Draw a picture that might be on the other side of the postcard, or cut out a picture and stick it here.

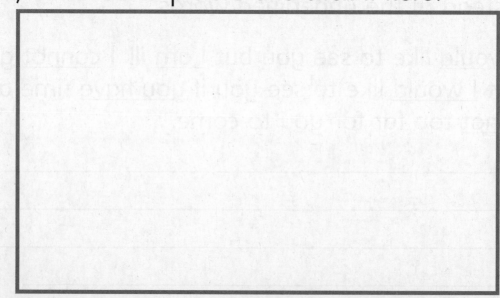

Speech bubbles

Look at what is happening in each picture. What do you think the people are saying?
Write the words in the speech bubbles.

Reading instructions

Read the instructions and then draw on the pictures.

1. Draw a hat on the first clown.
2. Draw long shoes on the second clown.
3. Draw spots on the trousers of the third clown.
4. Draw a flower on the hat of the second clown.
5. Draw curly hair on the third clown.
6. Draw a smile on the face of the first clown.
7. Draw a bow-tie on the first clown and the third clown.
8. Draw buttons on the shirts of the second clown and the third clown.

Note for parent: This activity gives practice in following instructions.

Silly or sensible?

Some of these sentences are silly, and some are sensible. Read each one and then write the word **silly** or **sensible** beside it.

1. A library is a place to borrow babies. _____

2. Clocks help us to tell the time. _____

3. All boys have black hair. _____

4. Teachers like to teach bananas. _____

5. Cats have baby puppies. _____

6. There are lots of animals at the zoo. _____

Now write two sentences yourself:

A silly sentence: _____

_____

A sensible sentence: _____

_____

Note for parent: In this activity your child can practise responding to different sentences.

25

Odd one out

Circle one word in each row that does not belong.

1.	Monday	May	Friday	Tuesday	Sunday
2.	square	triangle	circle	shape	rectangle
3.	paint	red	orange	blue	green
4.	sheep	horse	pig	cow	lion
5.	bus	car	man	lorry	van

Now put the words in the correct group.

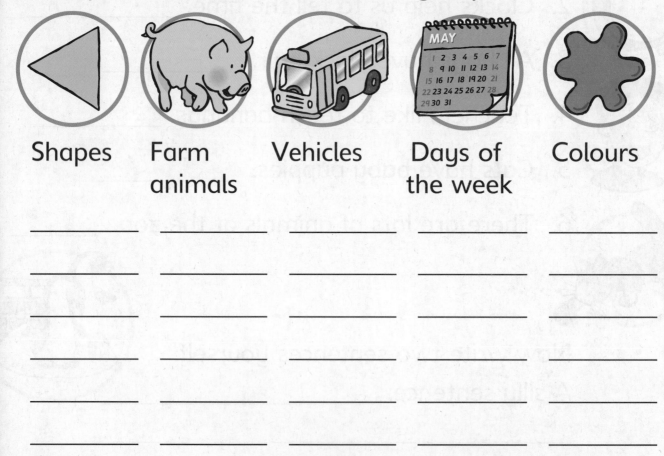

Shapes	Farm animals	Vehicles	Days of the week	Colours
_____	_____	_____	_____	_____
_____	_____	_____	_____	_____
_____	_____	_____	_____	_____
_____	_____	_____	_____	_____
_____	_____	_____	_____	_____

Can you add two words of your own to each list?

Quick quiz

Use an apostrophe to make these words shorter.

is not   I would   cannot

_____   _____   _____

Sort these words into the three boxes below.

**dog   tall   grows   soft   mouse
run   tree   cold   squeaks**

nouns (name words)	**verbs** (doing words)	**adjectives** (describing words)

Note for parent: This is a revision of some of the learning covered so far.

27

Opposites

An antonym is a word that has the opposite meaning to another word.

big   **small**

happy

sad

Read the words in the box.

| pull | near | dry | cold | full |
| hard | long | light | last | day |

Use the words in the box to write the antonym of each word in this list.

1. wet _____

2. soft _____

3. first _____

4. far _____

5. empty _____

6. hot _____

7. night _____

8. push _____

9. short _____

10. heavy _____

Note for parent: This activity helps your child to understand and use opposites.

Finish the sentences

Draw a line to join the beginning of each sentence to the correct ending.

1. The dog barked   into the air.

2. The horse galloped   a big web.

3. The frog jumped   on the wall.

4. The birds flew   at the burglar.

5. The spider spun   across the field.

6. The cat slept   out of the pond.

Now finish these sentences.

The dolphin jumped _____ .

The kangaroo hopped _____ .

Note for parent: This activity will help your child to use nouns, verbs and adjectives to make sentences.

Word search

Look for these words in the grid below.

nouns	verbs	adjectives
dog	runs	fast
tree	grows	tall
mouse	squeaks	soft

a	e	m	c	i	g	r	t	h	j
s	r	l	c	b	t	a	l	q	k
d	o	g	s	g	r	o	w	s	z
f	k	f	m	u	e	s	b	g	s
d	g	s	t	t	e	q	n	q	u
r	u	n	s	u	f	u	d	m	p
p	x	a	l	j	y	e	u	o	n
w	f	l	o	o	v	a	l	u	t
y	a	z	e	v	n	k	y	s	b
t	h	x	a	e	c	s	w	e	d

Now find all the letters of the alphabet and colour them red. There are 26 to find.

Puzzle page

Make as many words as you can from the letters.

p	o	r
l	e	t
i	s	a
r	e	m

You can move in any direction but do not jump a square.

_____   _____

_____   _____

_____   _____

_____   _____

_____   _____

How many words did you find?

Change one letter to make a new word.

man   _____   You cook food in this.

coat   _____   You go on water in this.

robber _____   You rub out with this.

card   _____   A horse can pull this.

fork   _____   Soldiers live in this.

wolf   _____   This is a sport.

Note for parent: These activities are quite difficult. Help your child by talking about the questions.

31

Answers

Page 5

Page 6

1. The <u>boy</u> is reading a <u>book</u>.
2. The <u>girl</u> is watching <u>television</u>.
3. The <u>dog</u> is playing with a <u>ball</u>.
4. The <u>man</u> is cutting the <u>grass</u>.

Page 7

1. A ladybird is very <u>small</u>.
2. The leaves fell off the tree because it was <u>windy</u>.
3. The sun was shining and the sky was <u>blue</u>.
4. Dad had just picked the flowers so they were <u>fresh</u>.
5. The dog was <u>happy</u> because he had a new ball.
6. It was <u>cold</u> in the garden and there was ice on the pond.

Pages 8-9

Page 10

fly, frog, coat, apple, balloon, lamb, bread, pear, queen.

Page 11

boy – A male child.
hutch – A pet rabbit's home.
monster – A creature you read about in fairy tales.
saw – A tool that has sharp metal teeth.
penguin – A black-and-white bird that cannot fly.

Page 12

top: sleeping, licking.
middle: running, climbing.
bottom: swimming, flying.

Page 13

two – 2, six – 6, three – 3, eight – 8, ten – 10, four – 4, seven – 7, nine – 9, one – 1, five – 5.

er   ce   ake   ar   tch   ing

Page 14

1. November. 2. January.
3. October. 4. July. 5. September.
6. May and December.

Page 15

<u>leaf</u>, sn<u>ail</u>, <u>peach</u>, <u>seal</u>, <u>pail</u>, <u>seat</u>.
<u>boat</u>, m<u>ouse</u>, c<u>oat</u>, cl<u>oud</u>, r<u>oad</u>, tr<u>ousers</u>.

Page 16

Possible answers are:
Dad is playing with a red ball.
The baby is eating a big ice cream.
The brown dog is chasing the cat.
Mum is feeding the hungry ducks.

Page 17

starfish, waterfall, homework, playtime, toothbrush, football, earring, bookmark.

Page 18

<u>bear</u> – <u>pear</u> – <u>wear</u>; <u>fire</u> – <u>wire</u> – <u>hire</u>; <u>jaw</u> – <u>claw</u> – <u>straw</u>; <u>brown</u> – <u>clown</u> – <u>crown</u>; <u>flight</u> – <u>bright</u> – <u>knight</u>.

Page 19

1. Kelly and Sam; 2. Sam and Anna;
3. Kelly and Anna; 4. Kelly and Anna;
5. Sam and Anna; 6. Kelly and Anna.

Page 20

1. Parrot said, "I like to fly and sing." 2. Monkey said, "I love to eat bananas." 3. Horse said, "I like to eat hay." 4. Kangaroo said, "I like to jump and hop." 5. Elephant said, "I have a long trunk."

Page 21

is not – isn't; cannot – can't;
I would – I'd; I am – I'm;
will not – won't; you have – you've.

<u>I'd</u> like to see you but <u>I'm</u> ill. I <u>can't</u> go out but <u>I'd</u> like to see you if <u>you've</u> time

and <u>it's</u> not too far for you to come.

Page 25

1. silly; 2. sensible; 3. silly; 4. silly;
5. silly; 6. sensible.

Page 26

1. May; 2. shape; 3. paint; 4. lion;
5. man. Shapes: square, triangle, circle, rectangle; Farm animals: sheep, horse, pig, cow; Vehicles: bus, car, lorry, van; Days of week: Monday, Friday, Tuesday, Sunday; Colours: red, orange, blue, green.

Page 27

is not – isn't; I would – I'd;
cannot – can't. Nouns: dog, mouse, tree; Verbs: grows, run, squeaks; Adjectives: tall, soft, cold.

Page 28

1. wet – dry; 2. soft – hard; 3. first – last; 4. far – near; 5. empty – full;
6. hot – cold; 7. night – day; 8. push – pull; 9. short – long; 10. heavy – light.

Page 29

1. The dog barked at the burglar.
2. The horse galloped across the field.
3. The frog jumped out of the pond.
4. The birds flew into the air.
5. The spider spun a big web.
6. The cat slept on the wall.

Page 30

a	e	m	c	i	g	r	t	h	j
s	r	l	c	b	t	a	l	q	k
d	o	g	s	g	r	o	w	s	z
f	k	f	m	u	e	s	b	g	s
d	g	s	t	t	e	q	n	q	u
r	u	n	s	u	f	u	d	m	p
p	x	a	l	j	y	e	u	o	n
w	f	l	o	o	v	a	l	u	t
y	a	z	e	v	n	k	y	s	b
t	h	x	a	e	c	s	w	e	d

Page 31

Some of the words you can make are: or, let, is, as, pea, at, mat, me. <u>man</u> – <u>pan</u>; <u>coat</u> – <u>boat</u>; <u>robber</u> – <u>rubber</u>; <u>card</u> – <u>cart</u>; <u>fork</u> – <u>fort</u>; <u>wolf</u> – <u>golf</u>.